Introduction to Composition

Workbook

WALCH PUBLISHING

Certified Chain of Custody
Promoting Sustainable
Forest Management

www.sfiprogram.org

SGS-SFI/COC-US09/5501

1   2   3   4   5   6   7   8   9   10

ISBN 0-8251-5575-4

Copyright © 2005

J. Weston Walch, Publisher

P. O. Box 658 • Portland, Maine 04104-0658

walch.com

Printed in the United States of America

WALCH PUBLISHING

Table of Contents

Table of Contents

Table of Contents

To the Student

Welcome! This *Power Basics® Introduction to Composition* Workbook is designed to be used with your *Power Basics® Introduction to Composition* student text. Each activity will help reinforce, extend, or enrich the material in your textbook.

 Reinforcement activities provide practice in what you have learned in the student text. These activities may be very similar to those in the textbook, or they may take a different approach to the content.

 Extension activities include a number of different approaches to the material and may "extend" the information a bit further. They may include critical-thinking questions, research questions, or real-life applications. In some cases, information that is covered briefly in the text is developed further in the extension activities.

 Since everyone learns in a different way, activities that invite the multiple intelligences are also included in this workbook. These activities help you connect to the material through approaches such as physical movement, partner and group dialogue and games, and visual respresentations.

Power Basics® is designed to give you the foundation you need to do well in school and beyond. This Workbook builds on the material you have learned in the student text and gives you a solid skills base to help you meet your academic and other goals.

UNIT 1 • ACTIVITY 1
Sentence Vocabulary

Match each word on the left with its meaning on the right. Write the letter of the definition on the line.

1. sentence _____
2. simple subject _____
3. complete predicate _____
4. fragment _____
5. complete subject _____
6. simple predicate _____

a. a group of words that forms a complete thought

b. an incomplete sentence

c. the main word in the subject

d. part of the sentence that tells what the subject does or is

e. the part of the sentence that tells who or what

f. the verb or verbs of the sentence

7. Underline the words from the list below that could be the simple subject of a sentence.

he	they	football	television
popcorn	skipped	Julio	sing
Anna	sew	we	spaghetti
oil	you	scamper	with

8. Write the correct words on the lines to finish the following statement. The simple subject of a sentence is usually a(n) _____ or a(n) _____ .

9. What part of speech must the simple predicate always be? _____

10. Underline the words from the list below that could be the simple predicate of a sentence.

will eat	are	skipped	eagle
car	ran	is singing	purple
wrote	window	listened	understood
if	have read	suggest	blurred

UNIT 1 • ACTIVITY 2
Subject + Predicate = Sentence

Write twelve sentences using the underlined simple subjects and simple predicates from Activity 1. Use one simple subject and one simple predicate to write a complete sentence. You may need to add more words to complete the sentence.

Example: Julio—simple subject; will eat—simple predicate

Julio will eat at the party.

Write twelve sentences using the underlined simple subjects and simple predicates from Activity 1.

1. _____

2. _____

3. _____

4. _____

5. _____

6. _____

7. _____

8. _____

9. _____

10. _____

11. _____

12. _____

UNIT 1 • ACTIVITY 3
Sentence Fragments

A sentence must have a subject and a predicate. A group of words with only a subject or only a predicate is a fragment. A fragment does not express a complete thought.

Some groups of words below are sentences, and some are fragments. For each sentence, write *sentence* on the line. For each fragment, write a complete sentence using the fragment.

Example: barks and jumps. The white dog barks and jumps.

1. The trash. _____

2. The pirate laughed at the parrot. _____

3. Running down the driveway. _____

4. In the bag. _____

5. Some actors. _____

6. You will answer the phone. _____

7. When the blanket was new. _____

8. The glass broke. _____

9. It was in my math book. _____

10. The man in the blue suit. _____

11. Mr. Wiggins and his son. _____

12. The frogs sat on a rock. _____

UNIT 1 • ACTIVITY 4
Dividing Lines

Each complete sentence is made up of two parts: a subject (who or what) and a predicate (what the subject does or is). You can easily divide most sentences into these two basic parts. Simply divide the subject from the predicate with a vertical line. For example:

Example: She | is reading by the window.

                subject   predicate

In the following sentences, divide the subject from the predicate with a vertical line.

1. The cat played with the ball.

2. The guys listened to the new CD.

3. The dinner was burned.

4. It rained all day yesterday.

5. The red pants were on sale for $15.

6. His new jacket was stolen.

7. I like ice cream.

8. The football game ended in a tie.

9. Charlie cut his long hair.

10. The line at the movies was very long.

11. My sister and I made dinner for the family.

12. Electra mowed the lawn Saturday.

13. The kids splashed in the water.

14. Susie did her homework.

15. Sean loaded the dishwasher.

16. Paula works at the pharmacy

17. The drama coach lost her temper.

18. The students stood when the bell rang.

19. Regina told a boring story.

20. The big dog drooled on my hand.

UNIT 1 • ACTIVITY 5
Word Addition

Each line below contains a fragment. Either the subject or the predicate is missing. In the space provided, write words that will complete the sentences.

1. _____ | had pizza for dinner.

2. Winter | _____ .

3. The coat | _____ .

4. Shopping | _____ .

5. _____ | is a hero.

6. _____ | is my favorite sport.

7. Green apples | _____ .

8. Angela's hamster | _____ .

9. The soccer team | _____ .

10. _____ | finished the test early.

11. _____ | gave their allowances to charity.

12. Olivia and Harris | _____ .

13. Angelina's textbook | _____ .

14. Yoko and Lydia | _____ .

15. _____ | warmed his hands by the fire.

UNIT 1 • ACTIVITY 6
Group Sentences

On the lines, write two complete sentences. In each sentence, divide the subject from the predicate with a vertical line.

1. _____

2. _____

Your teacher will label one section of the board "subjects" and one "predicates." In turn, write your subjects in the correct area and your predicates in the correct area on the board.

When everyone has written his or her fragments on the board, it is time to create new sentences. Make a new sentence by combining one subject and one predicate from the board. Your sentence should be as logical as possible. Make ten sentences this way. Write each new sentence on a line below.

3. _____

4. _____

5. _____

6. _____

7. _____

8. _____

9. _____

10. _____

11. _____

12. _____

Share your new sentences with classmates. Read your new sentence out loud.

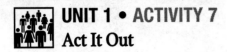

UNIT 1 • ACTIVITY 7
Act It Out

Sentences don't always have just one subject or just one predicate.

Examples: Bill and Bob play baseball.   Maria sings and dances.

                  2 subjects   2 predicates

Your teacher will divide the class into groups of one, two, and three people. Each group should act out one very simple scene. Your teacher may give you something to act out or you may choose a scene yourselves. For example, perhaps Anna and Lisa hop on one foot. Tony talks on the phone. After a group has performed, the rest of the class should create a sentence describing what the group did. A student or your teacher can write the final sentence on the board. Continue until every group has had a chance to act something out. Write each sentence below.

_____

_____

_____

_____

_____

_____

_____

_____

_____

_____

_____

_____

UNIT 1 • ACTIVITY 8
Order of Subject and Predicate

In most sentences, the subject comes before the predicate. In some sentences, however, the predicate comes first. Realizing that subjects can appear in different places in a sentence can help your writing two ways. It will help you vary your sentences to keep them interesting. It will also help you recognize the subject so that you can choose the correct verb.

Rewrite each sentence so that the subject comes before the predicate. Use a vertical line to separate the subject from the predicate in your new sentence.

1. After the rain comes rainbws.

   _____

2. In numbers is strength.

   _____

3. On the wall is a switch.

   _____

4. By the lake lived an old woman with coal-black hair.

   _____

5. Beneath all the trash gleamed a diamond.

   _____

6. There on the hill was the runaway horse.

   _____

7. Well-loved are childhood toys.

   _____

8. Once upon a time lived a beautiful princess.

   _____

9. On the table sat a bouquet of a dozen red roses.

   _____

10. "Ahoy!" shouted the captain.

   _____

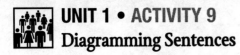

UNIT 1 • ACTIVITY 9
Diagramming Sentences

When you make a diagram of a sentence, you turn the words into a picture of sorts.

You begin by writing the simple subject and the simple predicate on a line. A vertical line separates the two parts. Look at this sentence:

The purple fish swam quickly.

The simple subject is *fish*. The simple predicate is *swam*. To begin diagramming the sentence, put *fish* and *swam* on a line like this:

fish | swam

But there are more words in the sentence. We can add them to the picture, too. The words *the* and *purple* describe the fish. These words are placed on slanted lines extending down from left to right from the word they describe—*fish*. Since *quickly* describes how the fish swam, it should be written on a slanted line that comes down from the word *swam*.

This is the diagram of the sentence *The purple fish swam quickly.*

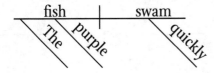

Here are a few sentences for you to try.

1. Small balloons fly high.

2. The girl is snoring loudly.

3. The moon is shining brightly.

How can diagramming a sentence help your writing? It can help you use the correct verb endings. If you start to diagram a sentence and see Jim | run, you should see that you have made a mistake. It should be *Jim runs.* You might see this mistake in a short sentence, but it might be hidden in a longer sentence. Diagramming can also help you keep a modifier close to the word it describes. In a short sentence, it may be easy to keep the modifiers in the right place. In a longer sentence, it is not as easy.

UNIT 1 • ACTIVITY 10
Clauses

Answer the following questions in your own words.

1. What is a clause? _____

_____

_____

2. What is a dependent clause? _____

_____

_____

3. What is an independent clause? _____

_____

_____

4. What is a compound sentence? _____

_____

_____

5. What is a complex sentence? _____

_____

_____

6. How are the independent clauses of a compound sentence joined? _____

_____

_____

UNIT 1 • ACTIVITY 11
Clause or Not?

Below are groups of words. Some are clauses. Some are not. Write the word *clause* on the line if the group of words is a clause. Leave the line empty if the group of words is not a clause.

1. The baby is crying _____

2. The candy bar is covered in white chocolate _____

3. When he entered the room near the stairs _____

4. Standing by the door _____

5. The telephone needs to be recharged _____

6. After the sick bird squawked _____

7. The church bell rang once _____

8. Candle on the table _____

9. The paper was folded into a star _____

10. Full of small pointed sticks _____

11. All six of the puppies were black _____

12. Racing down the road at the speed of light _____

13. The key to a successful career _____

14. The class cheered _____

15. Once the dust settled _____

Unit 1: Sentences • Introduction to Composition

UNIT 1 • ACTIVITY 12
Independent and Dependent Clauses

A clause contains a subject and a verb. It can be independent or dependent. An independent clause is a sentence. It is a complete thought. It can stand alone. A dependent clause does not express a complete thought. When you read a dependent clause, you feel like you need more information. Most dependent clauses begin with an introductory word such as *after, although, because, if, since, when,* or *while.*

Below are some clauses. If the clause is a dependent clause, write *dependent* on the line. If the clause is an independent clause, write *independent* on the line.

1. When the doorbell rang _____

2. We could have milk or juice with breakfast _____

3. Because it was raining _____

4. Since the storm washed away the road _____

5. If the basket is full _____

6. Before I measure the wood _____

7. The dog waited by the door _____

8. After the can of soda spilled _____

9. The chair squeaked _____

10. During the time he was in the pool _____

11. The long story made me laugh _____

12. Until the cake comes out of the oven _____

13. Smooth stones lined the path _____

14. Even though the runner ran his fastest time _____

15. While we sat in the hot bus on sticky seats _____

UNIT 1 • ACTIVITY 13
Compound Sentences

A compound sentence is made up of two or more independent clauses. The independent clauses are joined by a semicolon, or by a comma followed by a conjunction.

Example: Randy is from Ohio; Rick is from Texas.

Randy is from Ohio, but Rick is from Texas.

Below is a list of independent clauses. Choose any two independent clauses and join them to make a compound sentence. Do this eight times. Write each compound sentence on a line below. Remember two things. First, the sentences must make sense. Second, add a comma followed by a conjunction (*and, or, but*), or a semicolon to join the sentences.

The train was late.	Rona baked a tart.
The milk bottle is glass.	We had seen the television show before.
The dog barked loudly.	The flood made travel difficult.
Mary played soccer.	The old cat slept.
The car did not start.	There was no gas.
The sun set in the west.	Jeff swam.
The sunset was beautiful.	We went to the movies.
Brendan made brownies.	The soda bottle was plastic.

1. _____

2. _____

3. _____

4. _____

5. _____

6. _____

7. _____

8. _____

UNIT 1 • ACTIVITY 14
Complex Sentences

A complex sentence is made up of one independent clause and at least one dependent clause. As you read, you will probably notice many complex sentences. Complex sentences add variety to any writing.

The sentences below are all complex sentences. Underline each dependent clause.

1. When you go to the store, please buy onions and carrots.

2. He called while I was in the shower.

3. The plane was late because there was a bad storm along the route.

4. The boy with red hair sat in front of me until he left.

5. The game was interrupted when it started to rain.

6. After his team won the World Series, he couldn't sleep.

7. He stayed in bed until the alarm rang.

8. It has been four years since he was elected.

9. After the storm ended, the air smelled fresh.

10. He waited until the late bell rang.

11. Because she had to work late, she did not study very much last night.

12. She planned to stay until the last customer had left the store.

13. He finished the job because he had agreed to help.

14. While Judith stacked cans, Lauren wiped the counters.

15. Sandrine wanted a new coat since her sister got one.

UNIT 1 • ACTIVITY 15
Adding Complexity

We often create complex sentences when we want to add more information to a sentence. Add a dependent clause to each sentence below to make a complex sentence. Write your new sentence on the line.

1. The lights went out.

   _____

2. The music on the radio was very loud.

   _____

3. The red pen leaked.

   _____

4. I have already finished my history paper.

   _____

5. The cookie crumbled.

   _____

6. The cast learned their lines.

   _____

7. The cat yowled.

   _____

8. Simon played poorly.

   _____

9. Sabrina scored a goal.

   _____

10. The car stalled.

   _____

UNIT 1 • ACTIVITY 16
Running On

Answer in your own words.

1. What is a run-on sentence?

_____

_____

Read the sentences below. If the sentence is correct, write *correct* on the line. If it is a run-on sentence, write *run-on* on the line.

2. The dog barked he chased the robber away. _____

3. The radio station played the latest music. _____

4. Falling leaves can make a mess on the sidewalk. _____

5. Jack and Jerry played basketball at the park. _____

6. The restaurant was busy people had to wait for their food. _____

7. The lion roared and scared the boy. _____

8. It was a stormy night the wind howled. _____

9. The shoes were too small they hurt my feet. _____

10. The alarm clock did not go off we were late. _____

11. The new earrings pinched her ears. _____

12. Louie did not want to play he wanted to sleep. _____

UNIT 1 • ACTIVITY 17
Quick Fixes

One way to fix a run-on sentence is to separate it into two or more sentences. Look at this example:

RUN-ON	The runner did not stop he grabbed a drink and kept running.
CORRECTED	The runner did not stop. He grabbed a drink and kept running.

All the sentences below are run-on sentences. Read each sentence. Then fix it by making two shorter sentences. Be sure to add the correct punctuation at the end of each sentence and capitalize the first word of the new sentence.

1. The snow turned to ice it was hard to walk.

   _____

2. I like apple pie I eat it as often as I can.

   _____

3. He caught the football he ran across the goal line.

   _____

4. Her dress was dirty it needed to be washed.

   _____

5. Joe did not talk in class he was very shy.

   _____

6. The light burned out the room went dark.

   _____

7. Red is Gary's favorite color Ann likes blue.

   _____

8. The song was over everyone stopped dancing.

   _____

9. The store was having a big sale it was very crowded.

   _____

10. The smell was strong it made Kelly sneeze.

   _____

© 2005 Walch Publishing Unit 1: Sentences • Introduction to Composition

UNIT 1 • ACTIVITY 18
Another Option

You can fix a run-on sentence by breaking it into two or more sentences. You can also fix a run-on sentence by putting a semicolon between the two independent clauses.

RUN-ON   I have a cat Luisa has two dogs.

CORRECTED   I have a cat; Luisa has two dogs.

All the sentences below are run-on sentences. Read each sentence. Then fix it by using a semicolon to separate the independent clauses. When you fix a run-on sentence this way, you do not need to change any other punctuation or capitalization.

1. He didn't catch the ball it went into the tall grass.

   _____

2. These pants don't fit I have to return them.

   _____

3. Jim was first Maria was second.

   _____

4. Chicago is east of the Mississippi Denver is west.

   _____

5. Danny didn't call her she called him.

   _____

6. Mom read a book on the bus Dad read the paper.

   _____

7. A feather is light a brick is heavy.

   _____

8. We ate pancakes for breakfast we had a salad for lunch.

   _____

9. The coat is red the boots are black.

   _____

10. Juan played basketball then he went home.

   _____

UNIT 1 • ACTIVITY 19
Correcting by Joining

Run-on sentences can also be fixed in two steps. First, put a comma after the first independent clause. Second, add a joining word (*and, but, or*) at the beginning of the second independent clause.

RUN-ON   She likes chocolate ice cream he likes butter pecan.

CORRECTED   She likes chocolate ice cream, but he likes butter pecan.

All the sentences below are run-on sentences. Read each sentence. Then fix it by adding a comma and a joining word.

1. He likes rap music she likes jazz.

   _____

2. Ken was sick Tuesday Martha was sick Wednesday.

   _____

3. Mice are small elephants are huge.

   _____

4. George Washington was the first president of the United States his vice president was John Adams.

   _____

5. The television is broken you can listen to the CD.

   _____

6. I need gas for my car the gas station is already closed.

   _____

7. The football team has not lost a game the soccer team has not won one.

   _____

8. Al has English first then he has algebra.

   _____

9. The alien was powerful he did not know his own strength.

   _____

10. My new coat is so pretty it is not very warm.

   _____

UNIT 1 • ACTIVITY 20
Make It Complex

Sometimes run-on sentences work better if you do more than separate the clauses or add joining words and punctuation. You can turn the run-on sentence into a complex sentence by making one clause dependent on the other. Remember: Most dependent clauses begin with a word that leaves the reader asking for more information. Some of these words are *after, because, before, during, if, since, until, when, while.*

RUN-ON	The concert lasted a long time they were late getting home.
CORRECTED	Because the concert lasted a long time, they were late getting home.

All of the sentences below are run-on sentences. Read each sentence. Then fix it by making one clause dependent on the other. You will need to put a comma between the two clauses.

1. The spider dropped to the floor Nancy captured it.

_____

2. School was over she went to the library to study.

_____

3. The earrings were made of silver they sparkled in the sun.

_____

4. The refrigerator stopped working all the food had to be thrown away.

_____

5. I like sharp pencils I spend a lot of time at the pencil sharpener.

_____

6. I had only $10 I couldn't buy the shirt.

_____

7. The doorbell rang the dog was quiet.

_____

8. She dyed her hair it was a bright blue.

_____

9. The window was open the rug is wet from the rain.

_____

10. I couldn't sleep last night it was hard to get up this morning.

_____

UNIT 1 • ACTIVITY 21
Simplify

You will find many sentences that combine a dependent clause and an independent clause. Look in one of your textbooks and find five sentences that use this pattern. Copy each sentence below. Then rewrite the sentence into two separate sentences.

1. Original sentence: _____

   _____

   Two sentences: _____

   _____

2. Original sentence: _____

   _____

   Two sentences: _____

   _____

3. Original sentence: _____

   _____

   Two sentences: _____

   _____

4. Original sentence: _____

   _____

   Two sentences: _____

   _____

5. Original sentence: _____

   _____

   Two sentences: _____

   _____

UNIT 1 • ACTIVITY 22
Expert Solutions

You should now be an expert on fixing run-on sentences. There are more run-on sentences below. Use a variety of solutions to make them grammatically correct.

- Separate the run-on sentence into two sentences.

- Put a semicolon between the two independent clauses.

- Join the independent clauses with a comma and a joining word.

- Create a complex sentence with a dependent and an independent clause.

1. He won the race he got a big trophy.

    _____

2. I made the sandwich it doesn't have any tomatoes on it.

    _____

3. The new perfume cost a lot it still made me sneeze.

    _____

4. The door opened a juggler walked in.

    _____

5. The tree was as tall as the room it had to be trimmed.

    _____

6. The telephone rang Henry ran to answer it.

    _____

7. The ice cream melted a sticky puddle appeared on the floor.

    _____

8. The light hurt my eyes I blinked.

    _____

9. That is the oldest house in town it is more than 200 years old.

    _____

10. I got the mail there were two letters for Elizabeth.

    _____

UNIT 1 • ACTIVITY 23
Comma Splices

A comma splice is two or more sentences written as one sentence with only a comma joining them. A comma is not strong enough to hold two sentences together. You can fix a comma splice the same ways you fix a sun-on sentence.

COMMA SPLICE	Her shoes were green, they went with her dress.
2 SENTENCES	Her shoes were green. They went with her dress.
SEMICOLON	Her shoes were green; they went with her dress.
ADD JOINING WORD	Her shoes were green, but they went with her dress.
COMPLEX SENTENCE	Because her shoes were green, they went with her dress.

You can choose the solution that tells your reader exactly what you mean.

All of the sentences below have a comma splice. Use a variety of solutions to correct the sentences. Write the corrected sentence on the line.

1. Aldo weighed himself, he had lost five pounds.

   _____

2. Julie is in the office, she is leaving early today.

   _____

3. I like Brittany's new shirt, it is red with a white collar.

   _____

4. The waves hit the beach, the birds flew away.

   _____

5. The roller coaster is so tall, I can't see the top.

   _____

6. Kevin practiced serving, his dog chased the balls.

   _____

7. The desert floor was cracked and dry, it had not rained in months.

   _____

8. Her hands were covered in grease, the car was fixed.

   _____

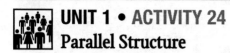

UNIT 1 • ACTIVITY 24
Parallel Structure

A sentence in which related words appear in the same grammatical form has parallel structure. A sentence with parallel structure can be drawn. It will look like a fork.

Example: Once upon a time, there was a king, his queen, and their lovely daughter.

	a king
Once upon a time, there was	his queen, and
	their lovely daughter.

Is there a pattern? Yes, all of the words on the points of the fork are nouns. Some have modifiers, but all are nouns. Therefore, the sentence is parallel.

Example: Running, swimming, and lifting weights are all good exercise.

Running,	
swimming, and	are all good exercise.
lifting weights	

Is there a pattern? Yes, all of the words on the points of the fork are verbs being used as nouns. Therefore, the sentence is parallel.

Write each sentence on the fork. Circle *yes* if a sentence has parallel structure. Circle *no* if it does not. If a sentence does not have parallel structure, rewrite it so that it is correct.

1. On her day off, she got a haircut, took a nap, and ate out.

    _____   _____

    _____

    Is the sentence parallel?   yes   no

2. When you don't get enough sleep, you feel stressed, get angry and concentrating.

    _____   _____

    _____

    Is the sentence parallel?   yes   no

3. Jim likes to play baseball, football, and running.

    _____   _____

    _____

    Is the sentence parallel?   yes   no

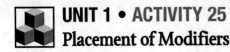

UNIT 1 • ACTIVITY 25
Placement of Modifiers

A modifier is a word or phrase that describes something else in the sentence.

Underline the modifiers in the sentences below. Draw an arrow from each modifier to the word it describes. There may be more than one modifier in each sentence.

1. The purple hat costs $15.

2. I got a cut from the broken glass.

3. The three men sat down.

4. His spiked hair is longer than mine.

As sentences get longer, it is easy to put the modifier in the wrong place. The sentences below have a modifier in the wrong place. Use the line below each sentence to rewrite the sentence to bring each modifier closer to the word it modifies.

5. The girl walked down the hall in a blue miniskirt.

   _____

6. That car is mine with the dents.

   _____

7. The tired swimmer rested after the race in his room.

   _____

Sometimes you have to do more than move the words to fix a poorly placed modifier. Sometimes you have to add or take out words to make the meaning clear. Use the line below each sentence to rewrite the sentence in a way that makes the sentence clear.

8. Turning the knob, the door opened.

   _____

9. After attending the concert, the music on the radio was boring.

   _____

10. Glancing at my watch, it was getting late.

    _____

© 2005 Walch Publishing

UNIT 2 • ACTIVITY 26
Parts of a Paragraph

Read the statements below. If a statement is true, circle *True*. If a statement is false, circle *False*.

1. A paragraph is a group of sentences.   True   False

2. A paragraph has one main idea.   True   False

3. A paragraph may have many sentences but it has three main parts.   True   False

4. The topic sentence tells what a paragraph is about.   True   False

5. Supporting sentences give more information.   True   False

6. There is usually more than one supporting sentence.   True   False

7. A concluding sentence ends the paragraph.   True   False

8. A concluding sentence restates the main idea.   True   False

9. In the paragraph below, label the sentences. Write *T* in the parentheses before the topic sentence. Write *S* in the parentheses before the supporting sentences. Write *C* in the parentheses before the concluding sentence.

   ( ) There is a wide variety of cereals at the grocery store. ( ) There is oatmeal for people who like hot cereal. ( ) Some cereals have fiber and extra vitamins. ( ) Other cereals already have fruit mixed in. ( ) There are also cereals that have fun flavors like chocolate and peanut butter. ( ) There are even cereals that make noise. ( ) There must be a cereal for everyone.

UNIT 2 • ACTIVITY 27
Cooking Up a Paragraph

Are you a good cook? Can you make a great sandwich? If you can, you can also write a great paragraph.

Topic sentence	⟶	bread
Supporting sentence	⟶	lettuce
Supporting sentence	⟶	tomato
Supporting sentence	⟶	meat/cheese
Concluding sentence.	⟶	bread

In the space below, explain how a paragraph is like a sandwich. Make sure you have a topic sentence, supporting sentences, and a concluding sentence.

_____

_____

_____

_____

_____

_____

_____

UNIT 2 • ACTIVITY 28
Magazine Mix-Up

All paragraphs are made up of a topic sentence, supporting sentences, and a concluding sentence. Choose one paragraph from your favorite magazine and identify the topic sentence, supporting sentences, and concluding sentence. Label them with a *T, S,* and *C* just like you have done before. Attach the article below. Copy each sentence onto a separate index card or sheet of paper (without labeling them). Pass out the sentences to other people in your class. See if they can put the paragraph back together and identify the sentences correctly.

UNIT 2 • ACTIVITY 29
Focus on Topic Sentences

What do you think when you meet new people? Do you want to know who they are? Do you want to know what they like? Do you hope that they will be interesting and fun?

A good topic sentence introduces you to a new paragraph. The topic sentence lets you know what the paragraph is about and why it was written. A good topic sentence should also be interesting so that people will want to read the whole paragraph.

A topic sentence should be focused. It should not be too general or too narrow. It should be just right.

Read each topic sentence. If the sentence is too general, write *G* on the line after the sentence. If the sentence is too specific, write *S* on the line after the sentence. If the sentence is a good, focused topic sentence, write *F* on the line after the sentence.

1. I can think of many good games for a teen birthday party. _____

2. Did you know that a magnet will not attract all kinds of metal? _____

3. You have several choices for lunch in the cafeteria. _____

4. Rocks are created in one of three ways. _____

5. The Declaration of Independence is a historical document. _____

6. Cleopatra was the daughter of a king of Egypt. _____

7. Blue whales eat about four tons of krill each day. _____

8. Most people have typical pets. _____

9. There are several ways to save money. _____

10. There are many ways to define freedom. _____

11. Do you know how to apply for a job? _____

12. Apples can be cooked or baked in various ways. _____

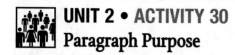

UNIT 2 • ACTIVITY 30
Paragraph Purpose

The topic sentence not only states the topic of the paragraph. It also tells the purpose of the paragraph. It tells why the paragraph was written.

In a small group, brainstorm possible topic sentences for the following general topics. One person should write down all the ideas from your group. Make sure the sentences are clear and well written.

Getting a driver's license

_____

_____

_____

Having an after-school job

_____

_____

_____

Exercising every day

_____

_____

_____

Tying school performance to money rewards

_____

_____

_____

When you are done, share your sentences with the other groups. As you can see, there can be many different topic sentences on any one general topic.

UNIT 2 • ACTIVITY 31
Topic Sentences at the Movies

Every day, many people write about the same topic. It is interesting because each person writes something a little different. Think about movie reviews. Each writer has his or her opinion and reason for writing.

As a class, decide on a movie that you would like to know more about. It should be one that many of you have seen. Look in newspapers, in magazines, and on the Internet for as many reviews as you can find. Read each review and underline the one sentence that gives you the topic of the review. Attach the reviews to this page.

In the space below, write the topic sentence for your own review of the movie. Make sure the sentence is clear and well written.

_____

_____

_____

_____

Compare your sentence to those written by others in your class. Does everyone have a different sentence? Can you tell who liked the movie and who did not? How can the topic sentences be made even more interesting? Discuss your ideas, then write some of your conclusions below.

_____

_____

_____

_____

_____

_____

_____

© 2005 Walch Publishing

UNIT 2 • ACTIVITY 32
Clarity

Clarity is important. Write the clearest topic sentence you can. Long sentences are hard to understand. Unimportant details make it hard to tell what the paragraph will be about. Short, simple words and phrases are easy to understand.

Each topic sentence below contains extra words. Read each sentence. Write a less-cluttered and clearer topic sentence on the line following each sentence.

1. You may never need to know this but butterflies are very different from moths.

   _____

2. Although it is nowhere near the largest city, Montpelier is the capital of Vermont.

   _____

3. There are many breeds of small dogs like Chihuahuas, pugs, Pekingese, miniature pinchers, and toy poodles.

   _____

4. It is not easy to smell the sweet smell of success in the field of gardening.

   _____

5. Mocha almond fudge is an extraordinary choice for a chocolate cake.

   _____

6. You should listen to the newest CD by The Bears because it is so very unique

   _____

7. If you plan your route before you take a car trip, you are much less likely to get lost.

   _____

8. Snow days with inches and inches of silvery flakes are the best kind of school days.

   _____

9. My grandmother was not able to descend down the stairs without help.

   _____

10. The important breakthrough came when the scientist accidentally spilled one chemical into another.

    _____

UNIT 2 • ACTIVITY 33
Supporting Sentences

Supporting sentences do most of the work in a paragraph. Once the topic sentence points them in the right direction, supporting sentences provide most of the information.

Circle *True* if a statement is true. Circle *False* if a statement is false.

1. All supporting sentences must have something to do with the topic.   True   False

2. Paragraphs should have at least three supporting sentences.   True   False

Below are some topic sentences and possible supporting sentences. Circle the letters of the three supporting sentences that best fit each topic sentence.

3. There are many spring flowers in the garden.
   a. There are tulips of many colors and sizes.
   b. Daffodils always add bright color.
   c. The snow still covers the ground in spring.
   d. Short flowers called snowdrops bloom early.

4. Learning to play the piano takes work.
   a. You need to practice
   b. Your fingers need to stretch to the right keys.
   c. You also need to keep the beat.
   d. You can make beautiful music.

5. There are only so many ways to close a coat.
   a. A belt can keep it closed.
   b. So can buttons.
   c. You can use a zipper.
   d. You need a warm coat in the winter.

6. In the high school, students can take many different math classes.
   a. I like math.
   b. Geometry is a math class about shapes and angles.
   c. There is a class to review the basics.
   d. In algebra, students have to find the value of *x* and *y*.

Unit 2: Paragraphs • Introduction to Composition

UNIT 2 • ACTIVITY 34
Brainstorming Is Fun

Brainstorming should be fun and creative. When you begin to write what you know about a topic, new ideas will come out of nowhere. You may not use all of your ideas, but some of the unusual ideas may be helpful.

Each sentence below is a topic sentence that needs supporting sentences. You do not have to write any paragraphs now. In the space after each sentence, brainstorm ideas for the supporting sentences. Write at least five possible ideas for each topic sentence.

1. Lunch in our cafeteria is never boring.

   _____

   _____

   _____

   _____

   _____

2. It's good to have extra pencils for a test.

   _____

   _____

   _____

   _____

   _____

3. Washing your hair is as easy as one, two, three.

   _____

   _____

   _____

   _____

   _____

4. My favorite sandwich is easy to make

   _____

   _____

   _____

   _____

   _____

5. There is a correct way to pack a backpack.

   _____

   _____

   _____

   _____

   _____

6. Math is my favorite subject.

   _____

   _____

   _____

   _____

   _____

UNIT 2 • ACTIVITY 35
Organizing Supporting Sentences

If you want people to read and like what you write, you have to make it easy to read. Using correct spelling and punctuation and writing correct sentences helps. Another way to make your writing easy to read is to organize supporting sentences in a paragraph so that they make sense.

Some common ways to organize ideas are

- in the order they happen
- from most important to least important
- from least important to most important

In the last activity, you brainstormed ideas for the topic sentences below. Look at those ideas again. For each topic sentence, choose three ideas that go together well. Write them on the lines below the topic sentence. Organize the ideas according to the directions in the parentheses.

1. Lunch in our cafeteria is never boring. (from least important to most important)

_____

_____

_____

2. It's good to have extra pencils for a test. (from most important to least important)

_____

_____

_____

3. Washing your hair is as easy as one, two, three. (in the order you do it)

_____

_____

_____

4. My favorite sandwich is easy to make. (in the order you do it)

_____

_____

_____

UNIT 2 • ACTIVITY 36
Writing Interesting Supporting Sentences

Some people talk using one tone. They never get excited. They never get sad. They never get loud. They never get quiet. They just talk on. Do you listen for very long? You probably do not.

People won't read your ideas if you just write on and on.

Do you know how to make your writing more interesting? Ask questions. Use short sentences. Include some sentences that are longer and more complex. Start your sentences with different words. Get excited and share it by using the most descriptive words you can. Get the idea?

You've already brainstormed for the topic sentences below, chosen the three best ideas, and arranged those ideas in the best order. Now it is time for you to turn those ideas into the three most interesting sentences you can. When you have three sentences you like, write them on the lines after the topic sentence.

1. Lunch in our cafeteria is never boring.

   _____

   _____

   _____

2. It's good to have extra pencils for a test.

   _____

   _____

   _____

3. Washing your hair is as easy as one, two, three.

   _____

   _____

   _____

4. My favorite sandwich is easy to make.

   _____

   _____

   _____

UNIT 2 • ACTIVITY 37
Sticking to the Topic

Sometimes it is hard to stick to the topic. There are so many interesting stories to tell and so many amazing facts to share. But, when you get off track, you confuse your reader. You make it hard for him or her to understand what is important. If you want to be a good writer, you will have to stick to the topic. If you are not sure, go back and reread your topic sentence. Every supporting sentence should be related to the topic sentence.

Because it is sometimes hard to tell if you are sticking to the topic, this lesson is best done with a partner. Look back at the previous lesson and the interesting sentences you wrote for the topic sentences below. With your partner, read each topic sentence and the three interesting sentences. Do you both agree that you stuck to the topic? Good. If you did, just write "I stuck to the topic" in the space below that topic sentence here. If you didn't, you and your partner should look back at your brainstorming. Find another idea that is better and write another interesting sentence together. Be sure to stay organized. Copy the new set of interesting sentences on the lines below.

1. Lunch in our cafeteria is never boring.

_____

_____

_____

2. It's good to have extra pencils for a test.

_____

_____

_____

3. Washing your hair is as easy as one, two, three.

_____

_____

_____

4. My favorite sandwich is easy to make.

_____

_____

_____

UNIT 2 • ACTIVITY 38
Ending with a Question

The concluding sentence is the last sentence of the paragraph. A good concluding sentence ties the whole paragraph together.

What do you do when you read a question? You probably answer it. That is why a question is a good concluding sentence. It makes the reader think about what has been said in the rest of the paragraph.

None of the paragraphs below has a concluding sentence. On the line after the paragraph, write a concluding sentence. Make sure it is a question.

1. Learning to play the piano takes hard work. You will need to practice each day. Your fingers must get strong and stretch to the right keys. You will also need to learn to keep a steady beat. When you play a song, you will have to know how to read music. You may also have to memorize a song.

   _____

2. In the high school, students can take many different math courses. There is a class to review the basics of math, such as fractions and percents. In algebra, students learn how to find the value of x and y. Geometry is a math class about shapes and angles. Students interested in practical math can take a consumer math class. Students can even take a calculus class.

   _____

3. There are only so many ways to close a coat and stay warm. A wide belt tied around your waist may keep the coat shut. A few buttons in a row will also work. A long zipper will let you close your coat just a little or all the way to the top.

   _____

4. There are many spring flowers in the garden. Short flowers called snowdrops bloom early. Then come the tulips in many colors and heights. Yellow daffodils always add bright color.

   _____

5. All computers have a few basic parts. A keyboard lets you type in information. The screen lets you see what you have typed. There is also at least one way to store information.

   _____

Was it hard to write a question for each paragraph? A question is not the best concluding sentence for every paragraph.

NAME:

UNIT 2 • ACTIVITY 39
Ending with an Opinion

Some concluding sentences give an opinion about the information in the paragraph. The concluding sentence tells what the writer feels about the subject. Sentences that have the words *in my opinion, I believe, I feel,* or *should* are usually giving an opinion.

These paragraphs still do not have a concluding sentence. On the line after the paragraph, write a concluding sentence that includes your opinion about the subject.

1. Learning to play the piano takes hard work. You will need to practice each day. Your fingers must get strong and stretch to the right keys. You will also need to learn to keep a steady beat. When you play a song, you will have to know how to read music. You may also have to memorize a song.

   _____

2. In the high school, students can take many different math courses. There is a class to review the basics of math, such as fractions and percents. In algebra, students learn how to find the value of *x* and *y*. Geometry is a math class about shapes and angles. Students interested in practical math can take a consumer math class. Students can even take a calculus class.

   _____

3. There are only so many ways to close a coat and stay warm. A wide belt tied around your waist may keep the coat shut. A few buttons in a row will also work. A long zipper will let you close your coat just a little or all the way to the top.

   _____

4. There are many spring flowers in the garden. Short flowers called snowdrops bloom early. Then come the tulips in many colors and heights. Yellow daffodils always add bright color.

   _____

5. All computers have a few basic parts. A keyboard lets you type in information. The screen lets you see what you have typed. There is also at least one way to store information.

   _____

Again, it may have been hard to write an opinion for each paragraph. An opinion is not the best concluding sentence for every paragraph.

Unit 2: Paragraphs • Introduction to Composition

UNIT 2 • ACTIVITY 40
Summarizing in a Concluding Sentence

Sometimes the concluding sentence quickly retells everything in the paragraph. This is called summarizing. When you summarize, you tell the main things but not every single detail. A concluding sentence that summarizes says the same thing that the topic sentence and the supporting sentences say—but in a different and shorter way.

Try writing a concluding sentence that summarizes these paragraphs.

1. Learning to play the piano takes hard work. You will need to practice each day. Your fingers must get strong and stretch to the right keys. You will also need to learn to keep a steady beat. When you play a song, you will have to know how to read music. You may also have to memorize a song.

    _____

2. In the high school, students can take many different math courses. There is a class to review the basics of math, such as fractions and percents. In algebra, students learn how to find the value of x and y. Geometry is a math class about shapes and angles. Students interested in practical math can take a consumer math class. Students can even take a calculus class.

    _____

3. There are only so many ways to close a coat and stay warm. A wide belt tied around your waist may keep the coat shut. A few buttons in a row will also work. A long zipper will let you close your coat just a little or all the way to the top.

    _____

4. There are many spring flowers in the garden. Short flowers called snowdrops bloom early. Then come the tulips in many colors and heights. Yellow daffodils always add bright color.

    _____

5. All computers have a few basic parts. A keyboard lets you type in information. The screen lets you see what you have typed. There is also at least one way to store information.

    _____

Again, it may have been hard to write a summary for each paragraph. Summarizing may not be the best concluding sentence for every paragraph.

UNIT 2 • ACTIVITY 41
Restate, but Don't Repeat!

Your concluding sentence can also restate the topic and purpose of the paragraph. If you do restate the topic and purpose, don't just repeat the topic sentence. You must find a new and different way to include the information from the topic sentence.

Restating the topic and purpose of the paragraph is often an easy way to write the concluding sentence. Restate the topic and purpose of the paragraph in the concluding sentence for each of the paragraphs below.

1. Learning to play the piano takes hard work. You will need to practice each day. Your fingers must get strong and stretch to the right keys. You will also need to learn to keep a steady beat. When you play a song, you will have to know how to read music. You may also have to memorize a song.

    _____

2. In the high school, students can take many different math courses. There is a class to review the basics of math, such as fractions and percents. In algebra, students learn how to find the value of x and y. Geometry is a math class about shapes and angles. Students interested in practical math can take a consumer math class. Students can even take a calculus class.

    _____

3. There are only so many ways to close a coat and stay warm. A wide belt tied around your waist may keep the coat shut. A few buttons in a row will also work. A long zipper will let you close your coat just a little or all the way to the top.

    _____

4. There are many spring flowers in the garden. Short flowers called snowdrops bloom early. Then come the tulips in many colors and heights. Yellow daffodils always add bright color.

    _____

5. All computers have a few basic parts. A keyboard lets you type in information. The screen lets you see what you have typed. There is also at least one way to store information.

    _____

It is usually possible to restate the topic and purpose of the paragraph in the concluding sentence. It is sometimes hard to make it different and interesting.

UNIT 2 • ACTIVITY 42
Your Opinion About Concluding Sentences

You wrote many different concluding sentences to the same paragraph. Which type of concluding sentence did you like best: question, opinion, summary, or restatement? Write your preference after each paragraph description.

1. For the paragraph about learning to play the piano. _____

2. For the paragraph about different math courses in high school. _____

3. For the paragraph about the ways to close a coat. _____

4. For the paragraph about spring flowers in the garden. _____

5. For the paragraph about computers. _____

Take a survey in your class. What was the most popular kind of sentence for each paragraph? Why? Explain your survey results below.

_____

_____

_____

_____

_____

_____

_____

_____

_____

_____

_____

_____

UNIT 2 • ACTIVITY 43
Concluding Ads

The concluding sentence is your last chance to convince your reader that what you say is true or important. Television and radio commercials try very hard to end with powerful concluding sentences. They want you to buy their product. You will not remember the whole commercial, but you may remember the last idea.

With a partner, write a five-sentence radio commercial about a product of your choice. The topic sentence should be attention-getting. The supporting sentences should give good reasons to buy the product. The concluding sentence should be easy to remember and make your listener want to buy the product. Once the commercial is written, practice presenting it in an effective way. Write your radio ad below.

_____

_____

_____

_____

_____

_____

_____

Take turns with other groups in your class and present your commercial to the class. What was the most popular kind of sentence for the concluding sentence: question, opinion, summary, or restatement? _____

Which concluding sentence did you like best? Why? _____

_____

_____

_____

_____

_____

UNIT 2 • ACTIVITY 44
Bringing the Pieces Together

Remember those paragraphs with supporting sentences you began in Activity 36? They still need concluding sentences. Look at your work one more time. Are there any changes or corrections you need to make? Next, copy your supporting sentences on the lines below. Add a concluding sentence to each paragraph.

Remember, you can use a question, an opinion, a summary, or a restatement in your concluding sentence.

1. Lunch in our cafeteria is never boring.

_____

_____

_____

_____

2. It's good to have extra pencils for a test.

_____

_____

_____

_____

3. Washing your hair is as easy as one, two, three.

_____

_____

_____

_____

4. My favorite sandwich is easy to make.

_____

_____

_____

_____

UNIT 2 • ACTIVITY 45
Types of Paragraphs

There are many types of paragraphs. Each one has a purpose. Draw a line from each type of paragraph to its purpose.

Type of paragraph

1. cause-and-effect paragraph

2. list paragraph

3. narrative paragraph

4. opinion paragraph

Purpose

a. tells a story

b. explains why some things happen

c. informs

d. explains a point of view

Read the paragraphs below. On the line at the end of each paragraph, write what kind of paragraph it is.

5. There are many kinds of dogs. Small dogs like pugs can live easily in an apartment. German shepherds and other large dogs often have jobs to do such as protecting their owners. Labrador retrievers and other sporting dogs like to help hunters. Cocker spaniels are good family dogs. There is a dog for everyone. _____

6. It was a long trip. The first day, we drove only 100 miles before we had a flat tire. The next day, it rained so hard we had to stop. On the last day, my little sister got sick. We really didn't go very far. It just seemed like it. _____

7. When I make popcorn, all sorts of interesting things happen. First, my house smells like a wonderful movie theater. Everyone in my family comes to get some popcorn and stays to talk a while. We all have a salty and buttery snack. Who knew making popcorn would be a family treat? _____

8. Chewing gum should be outlawed. Gum can have sugar in it and cause cavities. Gum is so noisy. Many people pop bubbles and chew loudly. Most people just throw their gum away. Then it gets stuck on my shoes or worse. The world would be better without gum.

_____

UNIT 2 • ACTIVITY 46
Cause-and-Effect Paragraphs

A cause-and-effect paragraph explains why something happened. Like all paragraphs, the cause-and-effect paragraph should have a topic sentence, several supporting sentences, and a concluding sentence.

This cause-and-effect paragraph has been started for you. The topic sentence is written. The concluding sentence is written. Write three supporting sentences to explain what happened. You may have to use your imagination, but each supporting sentence should be about an effect. Write the new sentence on the line

1. Drinking coffee that is too hot can cause many problems.

   _____

   _____

   _____

   _____

   Next time, wait for your coffee to cool a little more.

2. Many science and history topics are cause-and-effect events. Choose one you know about. Fill in the boxes below with causes and effects. (Add boxes if needed.)

cause	**effect/cause**	**effect/cause**	**effect/cause**

Now write a cause-and-effect paragraph using these events.

_____

_____

_____

_____

_____

_____

UNIT 2 • ACTIVITY 47
List Paragraphs

A list paragraph contains many examples to support the topic sentence.

This list paragraph has been started for you. The topic sentence and the concluding sentences are already written for you. Write three supporting sentences to help explain who helped the United States of America gain its independence from England.

1. It took the efforts of many people to create the United States of America.

   _____

   _____

   _____

   _____

   _____

   Many men and women worked hard for our country's freedom.

2. A list paragraph often introduces a new topic in a book. Look in a textbook and see if you can find an example of a list paragraph. Copy the paragraph in the space below.

   _____

   _____

   _____

   _____

   _____

Share your textbook paragraphs with classmates. What types of textbooks did most people use, or was there a wide variety?

UNIT 2 • ACTIVITY 48
Narrative Paragraphs

A narrative paragraph tells a story in a logical order. The details are often organized in chronological order—the order that they happened. A narrative paragraph can quickly tell what happened at an event or tell the high points of a person's life.

1. A narrative paragraph has been started for you. The topic sentence is written and the concluding sentence is written. Write three supporting sentences to tell what happened in a logical order. You may have to use your imagination, but each supporting sentence should be about something that could have happened.

   Saturday was one of my busiest days ever.

   _____

   _____

   _____

   _____

   _____

   I got a lot done on Saturday, but I sure was tired.

2. Narrative paragraphs are a wonderful way to introduce a topic. When you apply for a job, you should be prepared to tell the manager a little about yourself. Use the space below to write a narrative paragraph and tell an employer a little about yourself. Remember to begin with a topic sentence, add a few supporting sentences, and end with a concluding sentence. Be sure your supporting sentences are in a logical order.

   _____

   _____

   _____

   _____

   _____

   _____

UNIT 2 • ACTIVITY 49
Opinion Paragraphs

An opinion paragraph states an opinion and contains the reasons for that opinion. Opinion paragraphs are often hard to write well. It is easy to have an opinion but it is hard to explain why. When you write the supporting sentences in an opinion paragraph, choose your words carefully so that your reader will understand exactly what you mean.

1. An opinion paragraph has been started for you. The topic sentence and the concluding sentences are written. You just need to write at least three supporting sentences to explain why pet fish are wonderful. You may have to use your imagination, but your reader should want to head to the pet store today when you are done.

   I think fish make the very best pets.

   _____

   _____

   _____

   _____

   Everyone should think about getting a pet fish.

2. Everyone has opinions about many things.

   What is your favorite food? _____

   Who is your favorite performer? _____

   What movie was a waste of money? _____

   What sport is the most demanding? _____

Share your opinions with others in your class.

When you find someone who agrees with you, work together to write an opinion paragraph on that topic. Write the finished paragraph on another sheet of paper. Remember to begin with a topic sentence. There should be supporting sentences that include the opinions of both writers. End with a great concluding sentence.

UNIT 2 • ACTIVITY 50
Group Editing I

For a paragraph to make sense, it should be about one topic. Then the sentences should be well organized. There should be a topic sentence, supporting sentences, and a concluding sentence.

Work with a small group for this activity. Most of the sentences below are from two paragraphs. One is about Tibet; the other is about eye safety. There are a few sentences that do not belong in either paragraph.

In your group, decide which paragraph each sentence goes to. Put a *T* in front of a sentence about Tibet. Put an *E* in front of a sentence about eye safety.

_____ 1. You should also have your eyes checked by a doctor every two years.

_____ 2. A large part of Tibet is desert.

_____ 3. The average height is more than 3 miles high.

_____ 4. It is the highest region in the world.

_____ 5. You should rest your eyes from time to time.

_____ 6. It's in Asia, near India.

_____ 7. China is in Asia, too.

_____ 8. Eating foods like carrots and spinach can help keep your eyes healthy.

_____ 9. Everyone should take good care of their eyes.

_____ 10. Maybe that's why many people have never heard of Tibet.

_____ 11. One of the tallest mountains of the world is in Tibet.

_____ 12. You should know how to protect your eyes.

_____ 13. What do you know about Tibet?

_____ 14. Do you know how to protect your ears?

_____ 15. Very few people live there.

_____ 16. If you are doing something dangerous, you need to wear safety glasses.

_____ 17. You might also need a safety mask.

UNIT 2 • ACTIVITY 51
Group Editing II

Now it is time to write the paragraph about Tibet. Work in a small group for this activity. Use your list from Activity 50. It might help to copy each of the sentences about Tibet onto a separate piece of paper or an index card. As a group, decide on the topic sentence. What sentences best support the topic sentence? What order should those sentences be in? You can move the cards around until you find the best order. Do you have a concluding sentence? Move the cards around until you have a topic sentence, supporting sentences in a logical order, and a concluding sentence.

When you have the sentences in the best order, copy the paragraph on the lines below.

_____

_____

_____

_____

_____

_____

_____

_____

Taking turns, each group should have one person read its paragraph about Tibet to the class. Did all the groups agree on the best way to write the paragraph? If not, what differences were there? Write your answer below.

_____

_____

_____

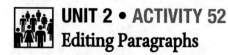

UNIT 2 • ACTIVITY 52
Editing Paragraphs

The sentences below all belong in one paragraph about a family breakfast. The sentences are not well organized. Decide what the best order is and number the sentences 1 through 7. The concluding sentence should be number 7. Use the space before each sentence to write the number.

_____ I wake up when I smell the tost.

_____ sunday breakfast is a big event.

_____ Dad gets up first he makes orange juice and starts fixing his special eggs.

_____ Then my mom started making enough tost for all of us.

_____ My job is two set the table.

_____ Then we all sits down for a great breakfast.

_____ My sister gets out the jelly.

The paragraph is pretty clear. We know how the family prepares breakfast and what they have to eat.

Is each sentence well written? Look for and correct any sentence fragments and run-on sentences by writing the correct sentence just above the incorrect one.

Is every sentence correct? Look for and fix errors in capitalization, punctuation, grammar, and spelling.

Congratulations. You have just edited a paragraph. Write the corrected paragraph on the lines below.

_____

_____

_____

_____

_____

_____

_____

UNIT 2 • ACTIVITY 53
Five Questions

There are five questions to ask yourself when you edit a paragraph.

1. Does the paragraph make sense?

2. Is the paragraph well organized?

3. Is the paragraph clear?

4. Is each sentence well written?

5. Is each sentence correct?

If you answer "no" to any of these questions, then it is time to make some changes.

The following paragraph has several errors and problems. Read the paragraph several times. Each time, try to answer one of the five questions below. Next to every "no" answer, explain the problem.

(1) Shoes are very important. (2) It is important to wear good shoes. (3) A comfortable pear of shoes makes it easier to walk wherever you need to go. (4) Shoes that fit your toes wiggle. (5) Your feet won't hurt so you well be in a better mood. (6) Shoes that look good will make you happy.

1. Does this paragraph make sense? _____

2. Is the paragraph well organized? _____

3. Is the paragraph clear? _____

4. Is each sentence well written? _____

5. Is each sentence correct? _____

6. Use the answers to the five questions to make changes. Rewrite the corrected paragraph below.

_____

_____

_____

_____

_____

UNIT 2 • ACTIVITY 54
More Editing

The following paragraph has several errors and problems. Read the paragraph several times. Each time, try to answer one of the five questions. You may make any changes in the space above the original words. You may use the ( ) to number the new order of the sentences if you want to make changes. When you have finished editing, copy the corrected paragraph on the lines below.

( ) Kath's room is very different. ( ) The ceiling is light blue the floor is painted as green as grass. ( ) The walls have big spots of blue and many shades of green.

( ) Kath's bedroom is looking like an indoor garden. ( ) Her bed and desk are made out of dark would. ( ) There is a tall light like a street lamp in the corner. ( ) Mounds of cloudlike white pillows are piled on her bed. ( ) Her closet door is painted to look like an arbor with vines growing on it.

_____

_____

_____

_____

_____

_____

_____

_____

UNIT 3 • ACTIVITY 55
Parts of an Essay

Answer the questions in your own words.

1. What is an essay? _____

2. An essay has three parts. They are _____, _____, _____

3. An essay is built from paragraphs. Below are the topic sentences from the paragraphs of an essay. Decide the correct order of the topic sentences. Build the essay by writing one topic sentence in each box. The first box should hold the topic sentence for the whole essay. The second, third, and fourth boxes should hold topic sentences for supporting paragraphs. The last box should hold the topic sentence for the concluding paragraph.

Metamorphic rocks are rocks that have changed into another kind of rock.

Igneous rocks are made by heat.

Each type of rock is made a different way.

There are three different types of rocks.

Sedimentary rocks have many layers.

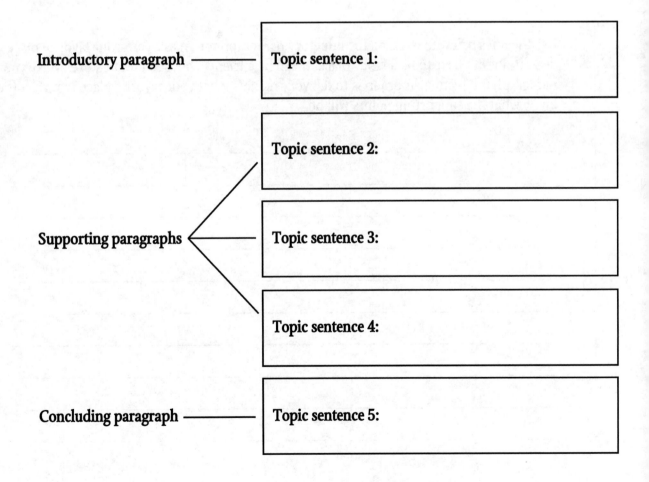

UNIT 3 • ACTIVITY 56
Introductory Paragraphs

Read each statement. If a statement is true, circle *True.* If a statement is false, circle *False.*

1. An introductory paragraph states the topic and purpose of the essay.   True   False

2. An introductory paragraph previews the supporting points.   True   False

3. The introductory paragraph catches the reader's attention.   True   False

4. An introductory paragraph can be short.   True   False

5. The topic sentence must be the first sentence of the paragraph.   True   False

6. The topic sentence can be anywhere in the paragraph.   True   False

7. Use the lines below to write an introductory paragraph for an essay on your favorite place to visit. It doesn't have to be a fancy place. It can be a friend's house or a fun store. Make your paragraph interesting. Your job is to tell your readers what your favorite place is and let them know what the supporting points will be.

_____

_____

_____

_____

_____

_____

_____

_____

_____

UNIT 3 • ACTIVITY 57
Grand Openings

Some books take a while to get interesting. Many good writers, however, know they have to write an exciting first paragraph for their book. They have to get their readers interested quickly.

Have you read an exciting book lately? Bring a copy of the book to class and read the first paragraph out loud for your classmates. Was the first paragraph exciting? What made you want to continue reading? With classmates, discuss what makes an opening paragraph interesting. Below, write some ideas that come out of the discussion.

_____

_____

_____

_____

_____

_____

_____

_____

_____

_____

_____

UNIT 3 • ACTIVITY 58
Great Expectations

The introductory paragraph of an essay should tell your readers the main points of the essay. One sentence should usually be enough to describe the topic of each supporting paragraph. Read the following paragraph.

There are often many types of ships in the harbor. Some are large working ships, such as oil tankers or cargo ships. Some are smaller working ships. Some are pleasure ships, including cruise ships and smaller family cruisers. There also are local motorboats. Every once in a while there are even rowboats, canoes, and kayaks in the harbor. It sure is a busy place!

1. What is the topic sentence of the paragraph?

   _____

2. What do you expect to find in the first supporting paragraph?

   _____

3. What do you expect to find in the second supporting paragraph?

   _____

4. What do you expect to find in the third supporting paragraph?

   _____

5. What do you expect to find in the fourth supporting paragraph?

   _____

6. What do you expect to find in the fifth supporting paragraph?

   _____

Granny is a great storyteller. Sometimes when we visit in the summer, she spends hours telling tales about the past. Read the introductions to three of Granny's stories below. Then answer the questions.

Have you ever wondered why Miller's Cavern is boarded up? Well, I know why. When I was a girl, youngsters sometimes played in there, looking for buried treasure and so on. One day, Wallace Klemper, a boy from around the bend, came running out of that cave with his hair standing on end and his eyes popping out of his head. He claimed he had seen a ghost.

1. How does Granny get her listeners' attention? _____

2. What do you expect the rest of the story tell about? _____

The weather could cause problems in all areas of life, even marriage. Renata and George were two lovebirds I knew as a girl. In those days, getting hitched at eighteen was common, so there was nothing unusual in that. The problem was that there was only one preacher for all the counties from here to Wollaston, and he only came around once in the winter.

3. What are Renata and George an example of? _____

4. What do you expect the rest of the story to tell about? _____

July 10, 1947, was the day I almost ran over your grandfather. It was the first time I met him. He surprised me by jumping out of the bushes. I had just learned to drive the big tractor, and I was a little shaky behind the wheel. I almost plowed him under that day.

5. How does Granny get her listeners' attention? _____

6. What do you expect the rest of the story to be about? _____

Now help Granny by writing an introduction for her. Try to get the listeners' attention so they will stay for the rest of the story.

She wants to tell about the time a nosy neighbor overheard her mother—your great-grandmother—saying she wishes Harvey were dead. The neighbor spreads this gossip. It turns out that Harvey was the pig that was to be slaughtered, and the mother had become attached to him. She was just wishing aloud that the butchering was over.

7. Write your introduction on another sheert of paper. Remember, you do not have to write the whole story. Just grab your listeners' attention, and then hint at what the story will be about.

UNIT 3 • ACTIVITY 60
Getting Attention

Let's look at two situations. You are eating something new for dinner. You take a bite. It is delicious. Do you eat more? Probably. Here's situation two. You are eating something new for dinner. You take a bite. It is tastes horrible. Do you eat more? Probably not.

The first paragraph of an essay must grab your attention just like that first bite of food. Look at the introductory paragraph you wrote. Will it grab the readers' attention and entice him or her to gobble up your writing?

You can use a specific example to introduce the topic. You may have to do a little research to write about a specific example. It will be worth it because readers want to know about real people and things that really happened.

1. What specific example can you use to introduce your paragraph about your favorite place?

   _____

2. If you had to write a report about the city or town that you live in, what specific example could you use to introduce an essay?

   _____

3. What specific example would you use to begin a report on your favorite band or singer?

   _____

You can start your paragraph with a shocking statement. Your reader will have to keep reading to see if it is true.

4. What shocking statement can you use to start your paragraph about your favorite place?

   _____

5. What shocking statement could you write to begin your report about your hometown?

   _____

6. What shocking statement could you write to begin the report about your band or singer?

   _____

Why don't you ask a question? Your reader will answer it. They will also keep reading to see what you have to say.

7. What question can you use to start your paragraph about your favorite place?

   _____

8. What interesting question can you use to start the report on the band or singer?

   _____

UNIT 3 • ACTIVITY 61
Keep It Short

Have you ever heard that less is more? Short, well-written sentences can hold a lot of information. Short sentences can be interesting to read. Long sentences and paragraphs can be confusing or boring for the reader. You can limit your introductory paragraph to three or four well-written sentences.

The paragraphs below would be more interesting if they were shorter and better written. Rewrite each paragraph to make it more clear and focused. Get rid of any unnecessary words and phrases.

1. Editing is a very important step in everyone's writing. Words that are spelled wrong should be corrected. Sentences that do not have the right punctuation should be corrected. Words that are not necessary should be cut out of your writing. Sentences that are not as clear as they should be should be rewritten. The result of editing should be writing filled with well-written sentences and paragraphs.

_____

_____

_____

_____

_____

2. Did you hear about the storm we had not today but yesterday at night? It was a cold, stormy night full of snow and wind. We drove our car home so slowly that a snail would have gotten home first. We couldn't find the keys that open our front door so we had to go to the neighbor's house. When my neighbor opened his front door to let us in, he did not have a smile that welcomed us. Even though he usually had a manner that was very cheerful, he was complaining about the weather. I was full of happiness when my dad got home and opened the door to let us into our house.

_____

_____

_____

_____

_____

UNIT 3 • ACTIVITY 62
Relevance

Supporting paragraphs should include only information related to the topic. The topic sentence of each paragraph is a guide to what should be in the paragraph.

Below are the supporting paragraphs from an essay. Cross out any information that is not relevant, or related, to the topic.

One of the simplest ways to create less waste is to reduce what you buy. Do you really need a new television when the one you have still works? New models do have new features. You can buy books and movies that you really like, but you can rent or borrow ones you will only enjoy once or twice. You may want to reconsider a habit of trying every new makeup brand or shampoo scent if you never use a whole bottle. Using plastic storage containers means fewer disposable bags to buy and discard.

You can also reuse what you own. A cracked plastic cup can hold pencils. A tablecloth with a big stain can become placemats with a little sewing. Pants that are too short can be turned into shorts. Shorts are cool. One good cooking pot can cook many different foods; you don't need special pots or appliances. You can use a pot to cook rice in and not buy a special machine. Plastic storage bags can be washed and used again. Plastic milk jugs can be cut to form scoops for pet food. You might want to make a bird feeder from an empty coffee can. Paper that you have printed on one side can be used by a young child for art projects. You can also cut the paper into small squares for notes. It is easy to reuse what you own if you think about it.

Recycling is another option. Paper, glass, and some plastics can go to a local recycling center. Not everything can be recycled. A younger brother or sister can probably wear clothes that no longer fit you. The clothes could also be given to a friend or a charity or sold at a garage sale. All sorts of things that you don't need can be sold or given away so someone else can use it. People will buy anything. You can also shop at stores with used clothes, books, and furniture. Recycling can help the environment and save you money.

UNIT 3 • ACTIVITY 63
Logical Organization

One way to organize paragraphs in an essay is in chronological, or time, order.

Words such as *first, after, next,* and *then* help organize events in the order that they happen.

1. What other words that tell chronological order can you think of? List them below.

   _____

   _____

2. Chronological order is often used to tell about what happened in history. Use the information about Martha Washington's early life to write a paragraph in chronological order. Remember to add an introductory sentence and a concluding sentence.

   Martha Dandridge was born in 1731 near Williamsburg, Virginia.

   Martha and Daniel lived on the Curtis plantation, which covered more than 17,000 acres.

   She also learned to run a house, sew, and cook.

   In 1757, Daniel Parke Curtis died, leaving Martha a widow at the age of twenty-six.

   When she was eighteen, she married Daniel Parke Custis.

   They had four children, of whom two died as infants.

   As a child, she enjoyed riding, gardening, dancing, and playing the piano.

   She had lessons in math, reading, and writing. Most girls did not.

   _____

   _____

   _____

   _____

   _____

   _____

© 2005 Walch Publishing

Unit 3: Essays • Introduction to Composition

UNIT 3 • ACTIVITY 64
How-To Know-How

Chronological order can also be used to explain how to do something. The steps for making a cake are listed below. Put the information in chronological order and use it to write a paragraph on how to make a cake. Remember to add an introductory sentence and a concluding sentence. Also, use words that show chronological order. Some chronological order words appear in the box.

before	first	then
after	second	next
finally	third	last

Frost the cake.

Preheat the oven.

Prepare the baking pan.

Cool the cake in the pan.

Pour the batter into the pan.

Carefully tip the cooled cake onto a serving plate.

Bake the cake.

Collect all the ingredients.

Enjoy your baked masterpiece!

Mix the ingredients.

_____

_____

_____

_____

_____

_____

UNIT 3 • ACTIVITY 65
Spatial Order

Spatial order is a way to describe how things look. Your words will create a map that shows where different parts or items are in relation to each other.

1. Words and phrases such as *left, right, behind, in front of,* and *next to* help tell spatial order. What other spatial words can you think of? Write them below.

   _____

   _____

   _____

2. When a person is described, the details usually start at the head and move down to the feet. Where might you start to describe a room? Why? There is more than one possibility.

   _____

   _____

   _____

3. What organization would you use to describe all the books in a tall bookcase? Think about giving a reader a picture of the bookcase.

   _____

   _____

   _____

4. What organization would you use to describe the contents of your backpack? With what item would you start? Why?

   _____

   _____

   _____

5. What organization would you use to describe your neighborhood? Where would your description start? Where would it end?

   _____

   _____

   _____

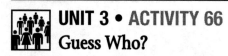

UNIT 3 • ACTIVITY 66
Guess Who?

Find an interesting photograph of a person from a magazine or newspaper. Do not show your picture to anyone in your class. On the lines below, write a logical paragraph to describe that person.

_____

_____

_____

_____

_____

_____

_____

_____

When you are done writing, give your picture to your teacher. Your teacher will put all the pictures from your class on the wall. When it is your turn, read the description out loud. Can the people in your class guess what picture you used? Can you guess what picture each of them used? Write your results below.

_____

_____

_____

_____

_____

UNIT 3 • ACTIVITY 67
Cause and Effect

Answer the following.

1. What are cause-and-effect paragraphs used for? _____

    _____

2. What are some words that help explain cause and effect? _____

    _____

3. Do you have a good sports team at your school? (If not, imagine that you do!) What does the team do to be successful? Write a cause-and-effect paragraph to explain. Remember to include an introductory sentence and a concluding sentence.

    _____

    _____

    _____

    _____

    _____

    _____

    _____

4. In science class, your textbook or lab manual tells you what steps to follow in chronological order to do each experiment. When you write a lab report about your experiment, you write about what happens and why. A lab report is a cause-and-effect paragraph.

    Imagine that you are explaining to first-graders what happens when you heat water in an open container. (It boils, giving off steam.) Explain the cause and effect in a few sentences for the younger students.

    _____

    _____

    _____

    _____

UNIT 3 • ACTIVITY 68
Comparison and Contrast

Writing a comparison and contrast is a little like writing a debate. Find a partner to work with on this activity.

1. Write two comparison and contrast paragraphs—one comparing things point by point, and the other treating each thing separately. Write your paragraphs below. You and your partner can agree on two things to compare and contrast.

_____

_____

_____

_____

_____

_____

_____

_____

_____

When you have finished writing, practice reading your paragraphs out loud. One person should speak the lines about one thing and the other should read the lines about the other side. Once you have practiced enough, perform your paragraphs for the class.

2. Which format did you like better? Why? _____

_____

3. Will that format always be better? Explain. _____

_____

UNIT 3 • ACTIVITY 69
Order of Importance

Answer the following.

1. When you organize ideas by order of importance, you have to make decisions. You can arrange the paragraphs in two different ways. What are they?

   _____

   _____

2. These paragraphs often use words to number the points. What are some words that would number the ideas?

   _____

   _____

   _____

3. You probably ask your parents for many things. Often they ask why you want something. That is a good opportunity to use order of importance.

   If you asked your parents for more spending money next week, what three reasons would you give? Use the lines below to write your answer. Be sure to use complete sentences and to list your reasons with the most important one first.

   _____

   _____

   _____

   _____

4. Now reread your paragraph. Underline the words you used to number or rank your reason. Would your paragraph be as effective without these words? Write your answer below.

   _____

   _____

UNIT 3 • ACTIVITY 70
Convince Me

Give reasons for each question below.

1. There seems to be an awards show on television every week. List five reasons why your favorite television celebrity should be named "the best on television." Be sure to use complete sentences. List your most important reason last.

_____

_____

_____

_____

_____

2. Most people write a list to help them make an important decision. They write down the reasons for acting and the reasons for not acting.

   Use the space below to write five reasons for going to college. Then write five reasons for not going to college. Be sure to use complete sentences. You may choose the order for your sentences, but use the same order for both parts.

   Reasons for going to college

_____

_____

_____

_____

   Reasons for not going to college

_____

_____

_____

_____

UNIT 3 • ACTIVITY 71
Concluding Paragraphs

Read each statement. If a statement is true, circle *True.* If a statement is false, circle *False.*

1. A concluding paragraph is the last paragraph of an essay.　　　True　　False

2. The concluding paragraph reviews the information in the supporting paragraph.　　　True　　False

3. The concluding paragraph convinces the reader that the essay has made its point.　　　True　　False

4. The concluding paragraph can add new information.　　　True　　False

5. There is more than one way to write a concluding paragraph.　　　True　　False

6. The concluding paragraph should repeat the topic sentence from the introductory paragraph.　　　True　　False

A concluding paragraph can summarize or tell the main points of the essay. It should use different words to state what has already been said. Below is a concluding paragraph. What points did each supporting paragraph that came before it probably include? Write the answers on the correct lines.

Concluding paragraph

Trying a new recipe takes some preparation. You first have to read the recipe carefully. Then, you must make sure you have all the ingredients. You may have to make a trip to the store to buy the ones you are missing. Last, you should check to see if you have all the necessary pots, pans, and utensils. Taking care of these things before you begin cooking will help you succeed in the kitchen.

7. First supporting paragraph _____

8. Second supporting paragraph _____

9. Third supporting paragraph _____

UNIT 3 • ACTIVITY 72
Questions?

A concluding paragraph can have questions. Questions can begin the paragraph, end the paragraph, or be anywhere in the middle. They will catch the reader's attention. Whether the reader wants to or not, he or she will try to use the information in the essay to answer the question.

1. Many people are speeding by your school every day. You have just written an essay to tell your town about the problem. You have to grab people's attention and get them to stop this dangerous situation. Write a question to begin the concluding paragraph.

   _____

   _____

2. The hottest part of summer will soon begin. Many homeless people have nowhere to go to get cool. You would like to help, so you have written a letter to your local newspaper asking for help with this problem. Write a question to end the concluding paragraph.

   _____

   _____

3. Your school has just started to recycle its trash. Used paper, drink cans, and vegetable scraps will now be recycled. You were on the committee that made this happen. Now, you need to get everyone to do his or her part.

   All students and teachers will get a letter asking for their help. Write three questions for the concluding paragraph. One should be about recycling paper. One should be about recycling drink cans. One should be about putting vegetable scraps in bins for composting.

   _____

   _____

   _____

   _____

   _____

   _____

UNIT 3 • ACTIVITY 73
Why Do You Think So?

A concluding paragraph may include an opinion that is based on the information in the supporting paragraphs. These paragraphs are written every day when movies and television programs are reviewed. The article will include many facts about the show, but the last paragraph or two will include the writer's opinion. The editorial page of the newspaper will also contain opinions about things that happen in the news.

1. Read a newspaper editorial about something that happened in your town or city. What happened? What is the writer's opinion? What words tell you that it is an opinion and not a fact?

    _____

    _____

    _____

2. Look at the Letters to the Editor section of the paper. This section contains letters written by people in your area. Anyone can write a letter to the editor. What are the letters about? Does everyone agree?

    _____

    _____

    _____

Everyone has opinions. To convince other people to agree with you, you need reasons and facts to support your opinions. What do you have an opinion about? Write your opinions in answer to the questions below. After each opinion, write three reasons for your opinion.

3. If I were president for one day, I would deal with the important problem of_____

    Reason 1:_____

    Reason 2:_____

    Reason 3:_____

4. The best thing about my school is _____

    Reason 1:_____

    Reason 2:_____

    Reason 3:_____

UNIT 4 • ACTIVITY 74
Brainstorming Ideas

Brainstorming helps you to find ways to develop a topic. The goal of brainstorming is to write as many ideas about your topic as you can. No idea is too small or too silly. Not every detail will be used in your essay, but you won't know which ones you will use until later.

Working alone or in a small group, use the space below to write a list of ideas about the general topic of baseball. You may use a separate sheet of paper if you run out of space.

_____

_____

_____

_____

_____

_____

_____

_____

_____

_____

_____

UNIT 4 • ACTIVITY 75
Narrowing the Topic

Look at your list of brainstorming ideas about baseball from Activity 74. Are there ideas that are more interesting to you than others? You may not be interested in baseball at all. You don't always get to choose the topic you have to write about. However, it is your job to find the best topics you can. They can be ideas you are interested in or ideas your reader is interested in.

1. When you narrow your topic, it is easier to write an essay. Choose three or four ideas from your baseball list that you like best and write them on the lines below.

_____

_____

_____

_____

2. Look at your short list of ideas. Do they fit together? Can you write a topic sentence and include all of the ideas? Use the line below to write your topic sentence. (If you can't write a logical topic sentence, you may need to choose a different group of ideas and try again.)

_____

_____

3. Do you have enough information to write a paragraph about each idea? You may be able to use some of your other ideas from your brainstorming list. Use the space below to make notes about additional information you might need.

_____

_____

_____

4. Where will you get this information? _____

_____

_____

By completing this lesson, you have organized your thoughts on baseball into the beginning of an essay. Each of the interesting ideas can be developed in a supporting paragraph in the middle of the essay. You will also need to add an introduction and a concluding paragraph.

UNIT 4 • ACTIVITY 76
Web Work

A web is another way to organize your thoughts when you are starting to write an essay. Let's make a web using your brainstorming ideas about baseball. The title is already written in the center of the web for you. In each large circle connected to the center circle, write a main idea. In the smaller circles connected to each large circle, write details that support the idea. Feel free to add circles or leave some empty.

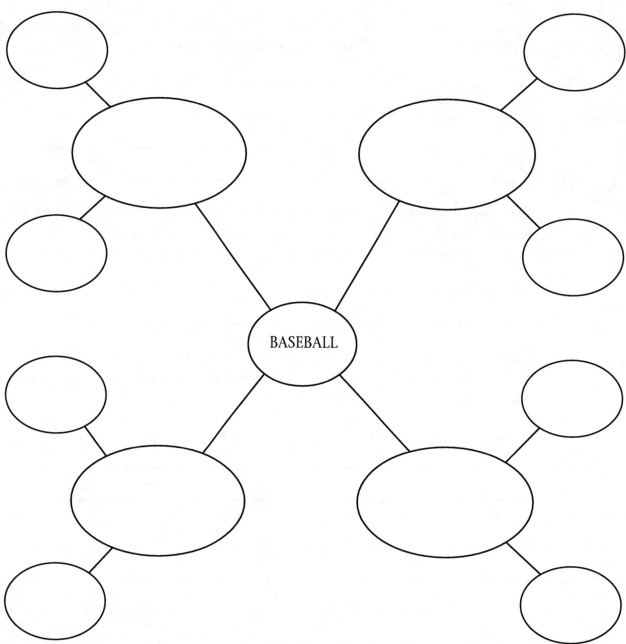

BASEBALL

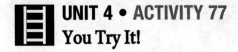

UNIT 4 • ACTIVITY 77
You Try It!

This is your chance. Choose a topic and brainstorm. You may choose a topic you like or you can work on a topic from one of your classes. If you can't think of a topic, here are a few suggestions.

dinosaurs	a television show	your state	space exploration
tornadoes	sharks	the President	your favorite movie star
your hero	airplanes	a favorite place	your favorite book

Choose a topic that you like and know something about. You will work with the topic in many activities to come. Write your topic on the line and use the space below to brainstorm.

Topic _____

Circle the three or four ideas you are most interested in. Could you write a report about those ideas? If not, see if you can find three or four other ideas that will work.

In future lessons, you will be asked to work with this topic. Any time you see the words YOUR OWN TOPIC, they refer to the topic you chose in this activity.

UNIT 4 • ACTIVITY 78
Weaving a Web

Use a web to organize your brainstorming ideas from YOUR OWN TOPIC. First write the title in the middle of the circle. Draw as many large and small circles as you need.

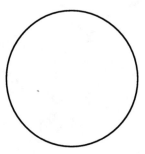

UNIT 4 • ACTIVITY 79
Outline Basics

Draw a line from each word on the left to its meaning on the right.

1.	brainstorm	**a.**	to narrow a topic
2.	focus	**b.**	a way to organize ideas in lines
3.	web	**c.**	a way to organize ideas using connecting circles
4.	outline	**d.**	write down ideas about a topic

Circle the correct answer.

5. Do you use sentences when you make a topic outline?   Yes   No

6. Do you use sentences when you make a sentence outline?   Yes   No

7. Which outline lets you include complete thoughts?   Topic Outline   Sentence Outline

8. Which outline uses short phrases?   Topic Outline   Sentence Outline

An outline organizes information in a way that is easy to read. It begins with a title that is *not* numbered. The main ideas begin with a Roman numeral. Do you remember how to write Roman numerals?

9. Next to each numeral below, write its Roman numeral.

1. _____   4. _____

2. _____   5. _____

3. _____   6. _____

    Unit 4: The Writing Process • Introduction to Composition

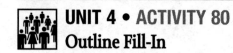

UNIT 4 • ACTIVITY 80
Outline Fill-In

You will find an incomplete topic outline in the left-hand column. Write the correct Roman numeral, capital letter, or Arabic numeral in the blank in front of each line. In the right-hand column, rewrite the outline as a sentence outline.

Air Travel Today

___ Reservations   _____

    ___ Travel agent   _____

    ___ Airline   _____

    ___ Internet   _____

___ At the airport   _____

    ___ Checking in   _____

    ___ Checking baggage   _____

    ___ Security checks   _____

___ On the plane   _____

    ___ Finding your seat   _____

    ___ Safety information   _____

        ___ Fastening seat belts   _____

        ___ Safety exits   _____

        ___ Oxygen masks   _____

    ___ The flight   _____

    ___ Landing   _____

___ At the airport   _____

    ___ Claiming baggage   _____

    ___ Ground transportation   _____

UNIT 4 • ACTIVITY 81
Outline Exercise

Now that you know the basics of how to write an outline, it is time to practice writing one.

Not all outlines organize information for an essay. You can also use an outline when you need to make an important speech. For example, your dad has just asked you to spend all day Saturday cleaning out the garage. When you tell him you already have things planned, he agrees to listen to your plans. If you really are busy, he'll take care of the garage. If you don't convince him, it's a long day in the garage for you. Use the space below to organize your thoughts into a topic outline.

My Saturday Plans

   I. My morning

  II. My afternoon

 III. My evening

Is your outline easy to read? _____

Did you divide the information into main ideas, supporting details and less important supporting details? _____

Did you indent each new level? _____

Did you use capital letters and Arabic numerals correctly? _____

If the answer to any of these questions is "no," correct your outline so that you can answer "yes."

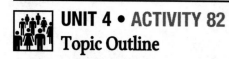

UNIT 4 • ACTIVITY 82
Topic Outline

Each time you make an outline, you will have a choice: topic outline or sentence outline? Sometimes a topic outline will be better. Sometimes a sentence outline will be better.

In the space below, create a topic outline for YOUR OWN TOPIC.

Is your outline easy to read? _____

Did you divide the information into main ideas, supporting details and less important supporting details? _____

Did you indent each new level? _____

Did you use capital letters and Arabic numerals correctly? _____

If the answer to any of these questions is "no," correct your outline so that you can answer "yes."

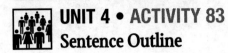

UNIT 4 • ACTIVITY 83
Sentence Outline

Maybe a sentence outline will work better for YOUR OWN TOPIC. Use the space below to create a sentence outline for YOUR OWN TOPIC.

Is your outline easy to read? _____

Did you divide the information into main ideas, supporting details and less important supporting details? _____

Did you indent each new level? _____

Did you use capital letters and Arabic numerals correctly? _____

If the answer to any of these questions is "no," correct your outline so that you can answer "yes."

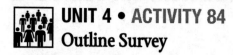

UNIT 4 • ACTIVITY 84
Outline Survey

Look at the two outlines you created in Activities 82 and 83. Decide which you prefer. Fill in the chart below with your preference and your reasons. Then ask five classmates which of their outlines they prefer, and why. When the surveys are complete, discuss the data.

Outline Survey

Name	Preference		Why?
	Topic	Sentence	

UNIT 4 • ACTIVITY 85
Creating a Topic Sentence from an Outline

When you complete any outline, it should be easy to see how your essay will be organized. The next step is to write a topic sentence for the essay. The topic sentence should tell your reader the purpose of the essay.

You have already worked on several outlines. Use the information in each outline from Activities 80, 81, 82, and 83 to write a topic sentence for each subject below.

1. Air Travel Today _____

   _____

2. My Saturday Plans _____

   _____

3. YOUR OWN TOPIC _____

   _____

Circle the answer.

4. Is each topic sentence broad enough to include the main points of your outline?   Yes   No

5. Is each topic sentence narrow and focused enough to give the readers a clear idea of the point of the essay?   Yes   No

6. Is each topic sentence clear and well written?   Yes   No

7. It should be easy to write a topic sentence from your own outline. Look once more at the outline you made for YOUR OWN TOPIC. Make any last minute corrections and be sure the outline is easy to read. Now, trade outlines with another person in your class and use the space below to write a topic sentence from his or her outline.

   _____

   _____

   _____

   Compare your topic sentence to the one your classmate wrote for that same outline. The two topic sentences are probably different, but they should both state the same purpose for the essay.

UNIT 4 • ACTIVITY 86
First Draft

Answer the questions in your own words.

1. What is a first draft? _____

2. Why should you write a draft? _____

3. Essays have three main parts. What are they? _____ ,

    _____ , and _____

4. What are the two jobs of an introductory paragraph?

    _____ and _____

5. In the space below, write an introductory paragraph for an essay about YOUR OWN TOPIC.
    The topic sentence you have already written should be a part of this paragraph. Remember to
    preview the main supporting points of your essay.

    _____

    _____

    _____

    _____

    _____

    _____

    _____

    _____

    _____

    _____

    _____

    _____

    _____

    _____

UNIT 4 • ACTIVITY 87
Strong Support

Supporting paragraphs make up the largest part of any essay. They flesh out the ideas you preview in your introductory paragraph.

Circle *True* if a statement is true. Circle *False* if it is false.

1. A supporting paragraph should develop only one point.   True   False

2. Each paragraph should be related to the topic sentence.   True   False

3. Supporting paragraphs should be logically organized   True   False
   so they flow from one to the next.

4. You should use transition words to connect your paragraphs.   True   False

5. Use the lines below to write the supporting paragraphs for YOUR OWN TOPIC. You may use another sheet of paper if needed.

_____

_____

_____

_____

_____

_____

_____

_____

_____

_____

_____

_____

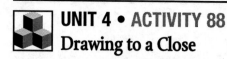

UNIT 4 • ACTIVITY 88
Drawing to a Close

You have almost finished your first draft. You have written the introductory paragraph and the supporting paragraphs. It is time to conclude your essay.

Review what you know about concluding paragraphs. Remember that the concluding paragraph may make a lasting impression on the reader. It is important to end an essay powerfully.

Read each statement. Circle *True* if a statement is true. Circle *False* if it is false.

1. A concluding paragraph should refer to the topic and purpose of the essay.   True   False

2. A concluding paragraph should repeat the introductory paragraph.   True   False

3. A concluding paragraph can summarize the supporting points of the essay.   True   False

4. A concluding paragraph can interpret the supporting points of the essay.   True   False

5. A concluding paragraph can add opinions about the supporting paragraphs.   True   False

6. A concluding paragraph can ask questions about the supporting paragraphs.   True   False

7. A concluding paragraph can add new information.   True   False

8. A concluding paragraph can restate the topic and important points of the essay in different words.   True   False

9. A concluding paragraph previews the important points of the essay.   True   False

10. A concluding paragraph is always the first paragraph of an essay.   True   False

UNIT 4 • ACTIVITY 89
Writing the Concluding Paragraph

It's time to finish the first draft of your essay. Use the space below to write the concluding paragraph for YOUR OWN TOPIC.

_____

_____

_____

_____

_____

_____

_____

_____

_____

_____

_____

_____

Check your paragraph by answering the following questions:

Does the conclusion refer to the topic and purpose in the introduction? _____

Does the conclusion summarize, interpret, add opinions, or ask questions about the supporting points? _____

Does the conclusion give the reader the feeling that you have made your point? _____

If you cannot answer "yes" to each question, reread your paragraph and make changes.

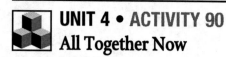

UNIT 4 • ACTIVITY 90
All Together Now

Congratulations on completing your first draft of your essay on YOUR OWN TOPIC!

In the past activities, you have written YOUR OWN TOPIC step by step. Use the space below to neatly copy your complete essay. You will find your introductory paragraph on page 86, your supporting paragraphs on page 87, and your concluding paragraph on page 89. Use an additional sheet of paper if needed.

Don't worry if your essay isn't perfect yet. You will have the chance to edit it in the following activities.

_____

_____

_____

_____

_____

_____

_____

_____

_____

_____

_____

_____

_____

_____

_____

UNIT 5 • ACTIVITY 91
Editing

Editing is the last step of the writing process before publishing the final piece. All the planning and organizing has been done. Editing puts the shine on your rough writing.

Answer the questions below about editing.

1. What is the purpose of editing?

   _____

   _____

2. Who should edit their writing?

   _____

3. When do you edit your work?

   _____

   _____

4. When you edit an essay, you work on one paragraph at a time. What are the five questions you should ask yourself about each paragraph of an essay?

   1. _____

   2. _____

   3. _____

   4. _____

   5. _____

5. You also have to look at the essay as a whole. What are three questions you should ask yourself about an essay you are editing?

   1. _____

   2. _____

   3. _____

UNIT 5 • ACTIVITY 92
Mechanical Errors

When you edit, you look for mistakes or problems. When you find one, you can use proofreading symbols to write the change. Mistakes in spelling, punctuation, and capitalization are called mechanical errors.

Match each symbol in the left column with its meaning in the right column. Write the letter of the correct meaning on the line.

1. sp _____   **a.** put in parentheses

2. p _____   **b.** capitalize the letter or word

3. ⌃ _____   **c.** spelling error(circle the word)

4. ⌣ _____   **d.** insert a comma

5. lc _____   **e.** punctuation error

6. ≡ _____   **f.** write in lower case letters

7. | _____   **g.** delete; remove

8. ℒ _____   **h.** transpose; change places

9. ∩ _____   **i.** insert space

10. ˇ _____   **j.** insert apostrophe

11. ⊙ _____   **k.** insert period

12. ( ) _____   **j.** close up; make one word

13. ^ _____   **k.** insert; add

UNIT 5 • ACTIVITY 93
Mechanical Fix-It

Read each paragraph below. Correct the errors using the proofreading marks for mechanical errors. Then write the corrected paragraph on the lines below.

1. Fall brings manny changes in nature First, it gets colder. The days also get shorter and shorter. Many plants turn brown. Then the leaves drop from the trees. animals begin to store food for Winter. others move to a warmer place. The world of outdors gets ready for winter.

   _____

   _____

   _____

   _____

2. I enjoy listning to the radio in the car. I can hear News and Weather any time I want Manny stations have traffic information that helps me get home quicker. Music makes any drive more fun. My car radio is a good Friend.

   _____

   _____

   _____

   _____

3. I love playing the piano. It requires practice, but the time spent is worth the results. I can play alone with a partner or with a recording. I can accompany myself when I sing. Playing the piano is more than a pastime it is a way to earn money. I hope to be a professional musician

   _____

   _____

   _____

   _____

UNIT 5 • ACTIVITY 94
Grammar Problems

Proofreaders look for grammatical errors in agreement and verb tense. Draw a line from the reference on the left to its meaning on the right.

1. vt   **a.** pronoun reference

2. s-v agr   **b.** subject-verb agreement

3. ref   **c.** verb tense

Each sentence below has a grammatical error. Choose a symbol from the box to tell what type of error each sentence contains. Write the symbol on the line.

vt	s-v agr	ref

_____ **4.** None of the students like the book.

_____ **5.** Bill swim and runs every day.

_____ **6.** Each person in our family makes their own lunch.

_____ **7.** She has already left for work when you called.

_____ **8.** Each of the parents are attending the meeting.

_____ **9.** Every student in the school are going to the game.

_____ **10.** Neither girl was pleased with their grade.

_____ **11.** Mina and Lucie shares their toys.

_____ **12.** The band played for an hour when the singer arrived.

UNIT 5 • ACTIVITY 95
Grammar Cure

Each sentence below has one or more errors in subject-verb agreement, pronoun reference, or verb tense. Find and make the corrections using proofreaders' symbols. Then rewrite each sentence correctly on the lines.

1. The red van went so fast he is a blur.

   _____

2. Every one of the police officers are dressed in blue.

   _____

3. Every student sat at their desk.

   _____

4. The cell phone that I used after the game are missing.

   _____

5. Mother wanted to find his new high-heeled sandals.

   _____

6. Neither Tomas nor Elvin can find their key.

   _____

7. Every writer wants people to read their stories.

   _____

8. Missy and Dot goes to the school on Main Street.

   _____

9. Mr. Paolo was in a rush and dropped her umbrella.

   _____

10. Tina reads Latin, and Ella wrote Greek.

    _____

UNIT 5 • ACTIVITY 96
Structural Weaknesses

Sentence structure errors include sentence fragments, run-on sentences, comma splices, parallel problems, and misplaced modifiers. Proofreaders' marks for these are written in the margin.

Write the proofreaders' symbol for the sentence structure error on the line following the type of error.

1. sentence fragment _____

2. run-on sentence _____

3. comma splice _____

4. parallelism problem _____

5. awkward sentence _____

6. error in sentence structure _____

Each sentence below contains an error in sentence structure. Tell what kind of error there is by writing the correct symbol on the line.

7. We saw a hot-air balloon walking through the park. _____

8. Saturday afternoons Jill takes piano lessons, plays soccer, and worked at the mall. _____

9. The whipping snow in a whirlwind around him. _____

10. The boy caught the ball, he ran away with it. _____

11. As he was going to work early one summer morning. _____

12. Today is the day tomorrow will be too late. _____

NAME:

UNIT 5 • ACTIVITY 97
Strengthen the Structure

The sentences below have sentence structure problems. Find the problem and write the correct symbol in the margin. Then rewrite the corrected sentence on the line.

1. _____ He will go to bed early, he is tired.

2. _____ Leaving the computer station.

3. _____ Sandy caught the pass he ran ten yards and then he was tackled.

4. _____ I couldn't believe it the cell phone died.

5. _____ It is important to read the directions this is a fragile instrument.

6. _____ He went to the mall, he did not buy anything.

7. _____ Tomorrow is her birthday she is looking forward to it.

8. _____ He tried, he failed.

9. _____ She dived for the ball she bruised her knee.

10. _____ After the final test, she grabbed her sweater, picked up her backpack, and run home.

11. _____ She read the book patting the dog.

12. _____ After all the hard work and time.

© 2005 Walch Publishing

Unit 5: Editing Essays • Introduction to Composition

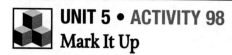

The essay below had several mechanical, grammatical, and structural problems. Use proofreaders' symbols to mark the errors.

Did you know that not all mountains are made the same way? Some mountans are folded some is dome-shaped mounds. Others are made by cracks in the earth. A few mountains are make by volcanoes.

The earth is made up of large movin plates. Where two plates meet, they push against each other The earths crust lift into ridges that fold over. When the ridges fall over, they break and make sharp, pointed mountain.

In some plates, pressure under the plaits stretch the earth's crust. At this weak spot, the pressure pushes the crust into a hamp. That hump becomes a round, dome-shaped mountain.

Sometimes the pressure causes cracks or faults in the crust. These cracks can be very depe and they can form longg blocks of dirt and rock. The pressure can cuz each block to move up down back and forth. Block-shaped mountains are formed this way.

Where the plates move away from each other, magma flows out into an emty space. When the magma hits air or water, it gets hard Little by little, mountains are made.

Plates and mountains are related. Two plates pushing against each other crate folds that become mountins. Underground pressure can stretch a plate and cause a dome-shaped mountain That pressure can also move bloks of the earth up and down to form mountains. Magma escapes from cracks between plates and slow builds a mountain. It take a lot of effert to produce a mountain.

UNIT 5 • ACTIVITY 99
Finishing Up

Rewrite the essay from Activity 98 with the corrections made.

_____

_____

_____

_____

_____

_____

_____

_____

_____

_____

_____

_____

_____

_____

_____

_____

UNIT 5 • ACTIVITY 100
Polish It Off

Often, when you look at your writing a few days later, you can see many silly mistakes. When you have to write a report, start early so you can take a break before you edit your paper. At the end of Activity 90, you completed a first draft of an essay. Now it is time to use your proofreading skills to correct that first draft. Use the proofreaders' marks to make corrections. Rewrite your corrected, polished essay below.

_____

_____

_____

_____

_____

_____

_____

_____

_____

_____

_____

_____

_____

_____

_____

_____

_____